The Official Spider-Man Annual 1998

Based on the smash hit animated series

Origination by Newsstand Services
Editor: Peter Nicholls
Design: Rob Sharp

Published in Great Britain by World International Ltd., Deanway Technology Centre, Wilmslow Road, Handforth, Cheshire SK9 3FB

Printed in Italy

ISBN: 0 7498 3386 6

CONTENTS

THE SENSATIONAL SPIDER-MAN

Peter Parker was a gifted but lonely student whose life was unexpectedly turned upside down that fateful day when he attended a science demonstration and was bitten by a radioactive spider. Amazingly, he found himself invested with the spider's proportionate strength, speed and agility.

Using his scientific prowess to devise his incredible webbing and web-shooters, Peter designed a costume for himself and became...the spectacular Spider-Man!

But in one of his first appearances as the web-swinger, he refused to apprehend a thief at a television studio...a thief who would go on to murder his beloved Uncle Ben. Peter's life would never be the same again. This tragedy taught him an important lesson, that with great power comes great responsibility.

Now, he seeks to right wrongs wherever he finds them as... **the sensational Spider-Man!**

STUDENT *PETER PARKER* GAINED THE PROPORTIONATE STRENGTH AND AGILITY OF A SPIDER AFTER HE WAS BITTEN BY A RADIOACTIVE SPIDER. ARMED WITH WONDROUS WEB-SHOOTERS AND COMMITTED TO USING HIS AMAZING POWERS FOR GOOD, HE BATTLES SOME OF THE MOST SINISTER SUPER-VILLAINS ON EARTH AS A SUPER HERO WHILE STRUGGLING TO LEAD A NORMAL LIFE AS PETER!

ADAPTED FROM HIS ANIMATED TELEVISION SHOW, THE STORY WITHIN THESE PAGES IS THE LATEST AMAZING CHAPTER OF... *SPIDER-MAN ADVENTURES*

...AND SO WE GATHER FOR THIS CEREMONIAL *GROUNDBREAKING* ON THE CAMPUS OF EMPIRE STATE UNIVERSITY--

--DELIGHTED IN THE KNOWLEDGE THAT OUR NEW *CRIMINAL SCIENCE BUILDING* WILL BECOME A REALITY!

A REALITY WHICH *YOU*, MY FELLOW NEW YORKERS, MADE POSSIBLE WITH YOUR TIRELESS EFFORTS.

ALTHOUGH I VIEW MY FINANCIAL CONTRIBUTIONS TO THE PROJECT AS MERE ENCOURAGE-MENT--

--YOU HAVE GENEROUSLY CHOSEN TO THANK ME WITH YOUR CHOICE OF NAME FOR THIS NOBLE INSTITUTION...

FUTURE HOME OF FISK SCHOOL OF CRIMINOLOGY

...THE *WILSON FISK SCHOOL OF CRIMINOLOGY.*

YET, IT IS I WHO SHOULD THANK *YOU* FOR ALLOWING ME THE OPPORTUNITY TO COMBINE MY PERSONAL INTERESTS...

...IN EDUCATION, PHILANTHROPY, CIVIC RESPONSIBILITY AND ABOVE ALL, AS OUR NEW SCHOOL DEMONSTRATES...

...LAW AND ORDER.

YOUR DAD SURE LOOKS PRETTY NERVOUS UP THERE, HARRY.

BY THE WAY, YOU SURE THIS APARTMENT THING IS OKAY WITH HIM?

AS LONG AS I PICK A ROOMIE WHO PULLS STRAIGHT A'S LIKE YOU, HE'LL PAY FOR EVERYTHING.

SO WHAT DO YOU SAY? ARE YOU IN WITH ME?

OUR EFFORTS HERE MAKE A CLEAR STATEMENT ABOUT THE VALUES WE AS CITIZENS MUST EMBRACE...

...A COMMITMENT TO IMPROVING THE QUALITY OF LIFE FOR ALL...

...FOR THE UNSELFISH CARING OF OUR NEIGHBORS...

I'M STILL WORRIED THAT AUNT MAY'S GONNA GET LONELY, BUT EVEN SHE SAID IT'S A GOOD IDEA.

AW, WHAT THE HECK? WHO CAN PASS UP THIS GREAT DEAL? SURE! I'M IN, HARRY!

COOL! ONCE YOU GET YOUR STUFF IN, WE'RE GONNA THROW A PARTY THE GANG'LL NEVER FORGET!

...FOR THE CONCERN OF THEIR WELFARE, AND ABOVE ALL--

--PROTECTION FROM THE CRIMINAL ELEMENT THAT PREYS UPON EACH OF US!

WHOA! SPIDER-SENSE GOING OFF!

GOOD LORD! WHO IS THAT--?!

HA-HA HA HA HA HA

HAHAHA HAHA!

THE HOBGOBLIN: BAD LUCK & TROUBLE!

SPRINNG

NEL YOMTOV
WRITER
ALEX SAVIUK
PENCILER
ROB STULL
INKER
STEVE DUTRO
LETTERER
KEVIN TINSLEY
COLORIST
SARRA MOSSOFF
EDITOR
BOB BUDIANSKY
GREAT PUMPKIN

FREELY ADAPTED FROM A STORY BY JOHN SEMPER AND THE TELEPLAY BY LARRY BRODY.

IT'S GOOD TO SEE THAT EVEN CERTAIN *DEATH* CAN'T DULL YOUR REPUTATION OF BEING A PUNSTER.

OKAY, THEN LET'S GET *SERIOUS*, HOBBY.

WHY ARE YOU AFTER *FISK*?

SORRY. NO TIME FOR THE "INQUIRING MIND" ROUTINE.

INSTEAD, SPIDER-MAN...

...IT'S TIME TO RIDE!

ENJOY THE FLIGHT! AND REMEMBER TO BUCKLE UP-- IT'S THE *LAW*!

SOME FLIGHT. NO SNACKS, NO MOVIE AND--

Uh-OH. DANGER AT TWELVE O'CLOCK HIGH...

THANKS FOR RIDING HOBGOBLIN AIR. 'BYE NOW.

HATE TO CUT THIS RIDE SHORT, CAPTAIN--

--BUT TODAY'S MENU DOESN'T CALL FOR "SPIDER-ON-A-STICK"! I'M OUTTA HERE... NOW!

SORRY I CAN'T STAY, SPIDER-MAN, BUT BUSINESS CALLS! HAPPY LANDINGS!

BAILED OUT JUST IN TIME! NOW TO CATCH A PASSING I-BEAM!

BOY! I COULDN'T EVEN LAY A GLOVE ON HIM! WHERE DID HE COME FROM?

AND HOW AM I SUPPOSED TO GET 'IM TO GO BACK?

THE INTERBOROUGH MEDICAL CENTER...

HOW IS SHE, DR. SHAFFNER?

SHE'S SUFFERED A FORM OF SEIZURE BROUGHT ON BY EXTREME STRESS. HER MIND IS RETREATING INTO ITSELF.

WE'VE DONE ALL WE CAN.

NOW WE WAIT... AND PRAY.

THANKS, DOCTOR.

PLEASE STOP BY MY OFFICE BEFORE YOU LEAVE.

THE POLICE ARE WAITING TO QUESTION YOU ABOUT ALL OF THIS. SEE YOU SOON.

WHY DO THE PEOPLE I LOVE ALWAYS GET HURT WHEN I'M JUST TRYING TO DO THE RIGHT THING?

NOT ONLY AM I RESPONSIBLE FOR AUNT MAY, BUT HARRY'S BEEN KIDNAPPED BY THAT MANIAC.

I CAN SEE WHY HOBGOBLIN WANTED REVENGE ON ME... BUT HOW COULD HE HAVE KNOWN WHERE I LIVED?

AND WHAT DID HE MEAN BY "GETTING TWO BIRDS WITH ONE STONE"?

WAIT... OF COURSE! HE WASN'T AFTER ME! HE WAS AFTER HARRY!

AND THAT GIVES SPIDER-MAN A PLACE TO BEGIN...!

NEARBY...

NORMAN OSBORN HARDLY EVER HAS TIME TO SEE HIS OWN SON, LET ALONE AN UNEXPECTED VISITOR LIKE ME.

BUT SOMEONE'S GOT TO MAKE HIM AWARE OF THE DANGER THAT HARRY'S IN.

FOR BETTER OR WORSE, THAT "SOMEONE" IS ME...

I KNOW OSBORN'S BEEN INVOLVED IN SOME SHADY DEALINGS, BUT EVEN HE CAN'T IMAGINE WHAT A NUTJOB THIS HOBGOBLIN IS.

JUST HOPE HE BELIEVES ME...

WHAT? UP THERE! SHOUTING TO SOMEONE IN THAT OFFICE! IT'S...

...HOBGOBLIN!

PERFECT, NORM! YOU GENIUSES ALWAYS HAVE A BETTER MODEL READY TO ROLL!

TRUST ME, YOU'RE NOT GONNA REGRET OUR NEW DEAL-- PARTNER!

HUH--?

WHAT'S THAT ALL ABOUT? OSBORN KNOWS HOBGOBLIN?

AND HE'S DOING BUSINESS WITH HIM?

IT'S TIME TO STOP ASKING QUESTIONS...

AND TIME TO START GETTING ANSWERS...!

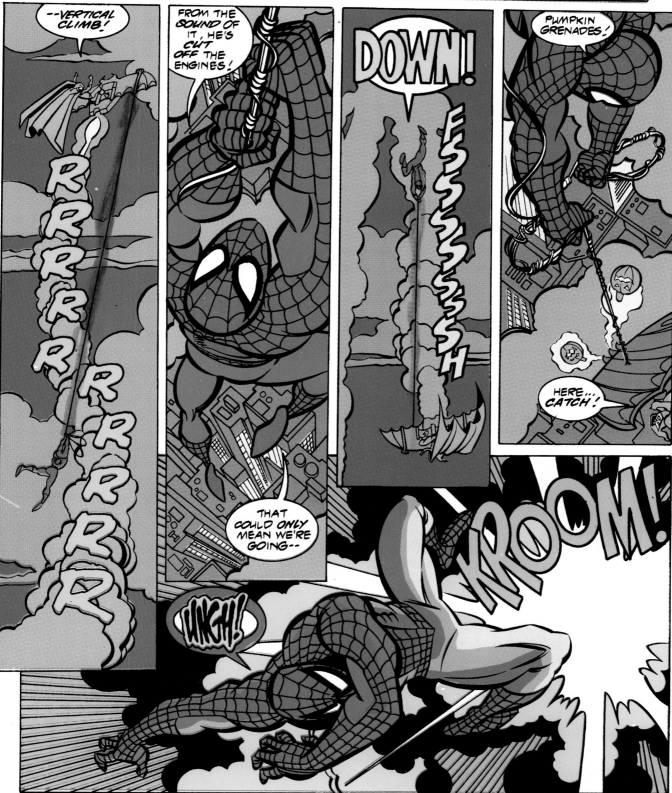

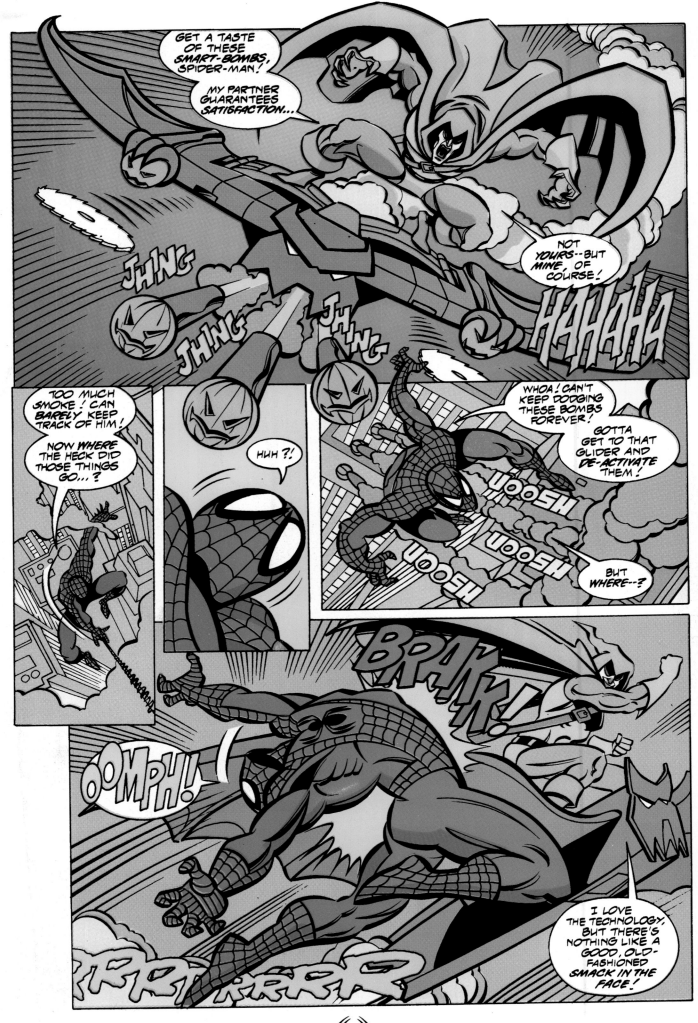

CONTINUED ON PAGE 30!

SPIDER-MAN

REAL NAME: Peter Parker

HEIGHT: 5' 10"

POWERS: Spider-Man has the proportionate strength, speed and agility of a spider. He gained his amazing spider-powers when he attended a science demonstration at college and was bitten by a radioactive spider. He has heightened reflexes and is able to cling to any surface, including walls and ceilings. In times of danger, his spider-sense tingles as a warning.

FRIENDS AND FAMILY: After the death of his parents, Peter was raised by his Aunt May and Uncle Ben. The tragic death of his Uncle Ben taught him that with great power comes great responsibility. His girlfriend is fellow college student, the vivacious Mary Jane Watson, and his best friend is Harry Osborn, whose father is secretly one of Spidey's most dangerous enemies, the Green Goblin.

COSTUME FEATURES: Spider-Man designed his costume himself. The eye-pieces in his mask are one-way lenses which allow him to see out but no-one can see in. He swings through the city and traps his enemies using the amazing webbing which he fires from his web-shooters, worn around his wrists.

The spider signal projector is hidden in Spidey's belt, along with the camera which he uses for photographing his fights with his enemies. As Peter Parker, he earns his living as a freelance photographer by selling these pictures to the Daily Bugle's irritable publisher, J. Jonah Jameson.

ENEMIES: Spider-Man has come to blows with a colourful assortment of fearsome foes, including the Lizard, the Shocker, Doctor Octopus, the Kingpin, the Green Goblin and the Hobgoblin. Lucky he has his spider-sense!

SPIDER-MAN

FACT FILE

THE KINGPIN

REAL NAME: Wilson Fisk

OCCUPATION: Criminal mastermind

BASE OF OPERATIONS:
The Chrysler Building, New York

WEAPONS: The Kingpin is completely bald and seems a little on the chubby side, but what appears to be fat is actually 100% muscle. His diamond tie pin fires sleeping gas and his walking stick shoots deadly laser beams.

ALLIES: The Rhino, the Shocker, the Hobgoblin and techno-genius Alistair Smythe

THE HOBGOBLIN

REAL NAME: Unknown

OCCUPATION: Professional criminal

BASE OF OPERATIONS: A secret location

WEAPONS: Deadly pumpkin bombs which can be fired from his Goblin Glider. He possesses superhuman speed and strength, together with greatly enhanced intelligence.

ALLIES: None. He works for whoever pays the most.

SPIDER-MAN

FACT FILES

STUDENT *PETER PARKER* GAINED THE PROPORTIONATE STRENGTH AND AGILITY OF A SPIDER AFTER HE WAS BITTEN BY A RADIOACTIVE SPIDER. ARMED WITH WONDROUS WEB-SHOOTERS AND COMMITTED TO USING HIS AMAZING POWERS FOR GOOD, HE BATTLES SOME OF THE MOST SINISTER SUPER-VILLAINS ON EARTH AS A SUPER HERO WHILE STRUGGLING TO LEAD A NORMAL LIFE AS PETER!

ADAPTED FROM HIS ANIMATED TELEVISION SHOW, THE STORY WITHIN THESE PAGES IS THE LATEST AMAZING CHAPTER OF... *SPIDER-MAN* ADVENTURES

STRANG DOOM

TAKIN' IT TO THE STREETS

A SPECIAL *FIRST-YEAR ANNIVERSARY* BLOW-OUT BROUGHT TO YOU BY:

| NEL YOMTOV WRITER | ALEX SAVIUK PENCILER | ROB STULL INKER | STEVE DUTRO LETTERER | KEVIN TINSLEY COLORIST | SARRA MOSSOFF & BOB BUDIANSKY DETONATION SQUAD |

FREELY ADAPTED FROM THE STORY AND TELEPLAY BY STAN BERKOWITZ

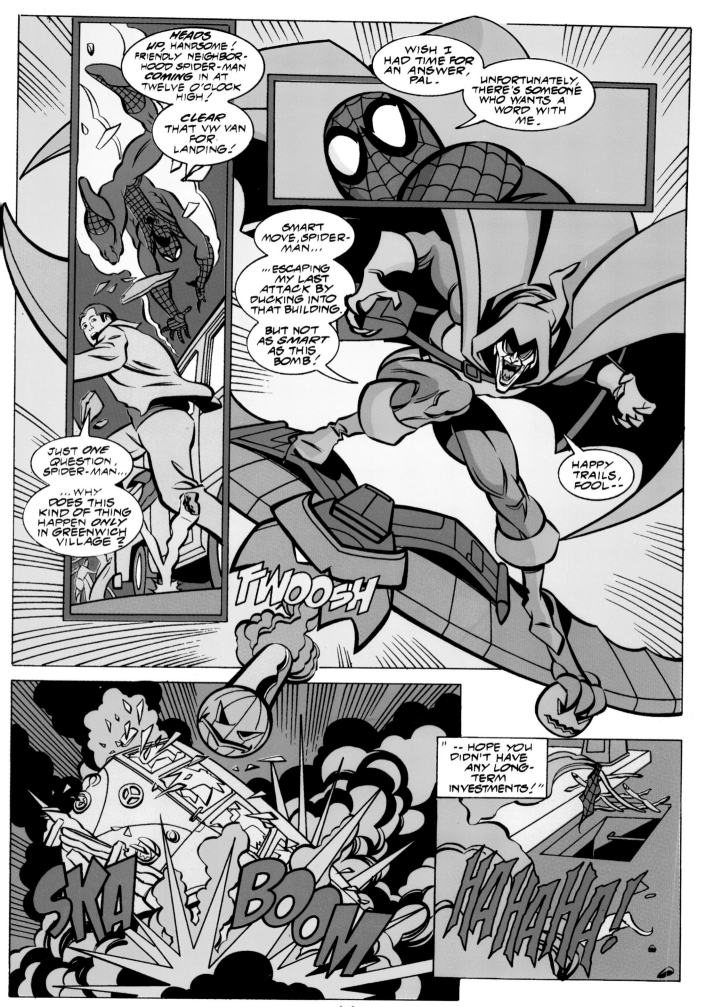

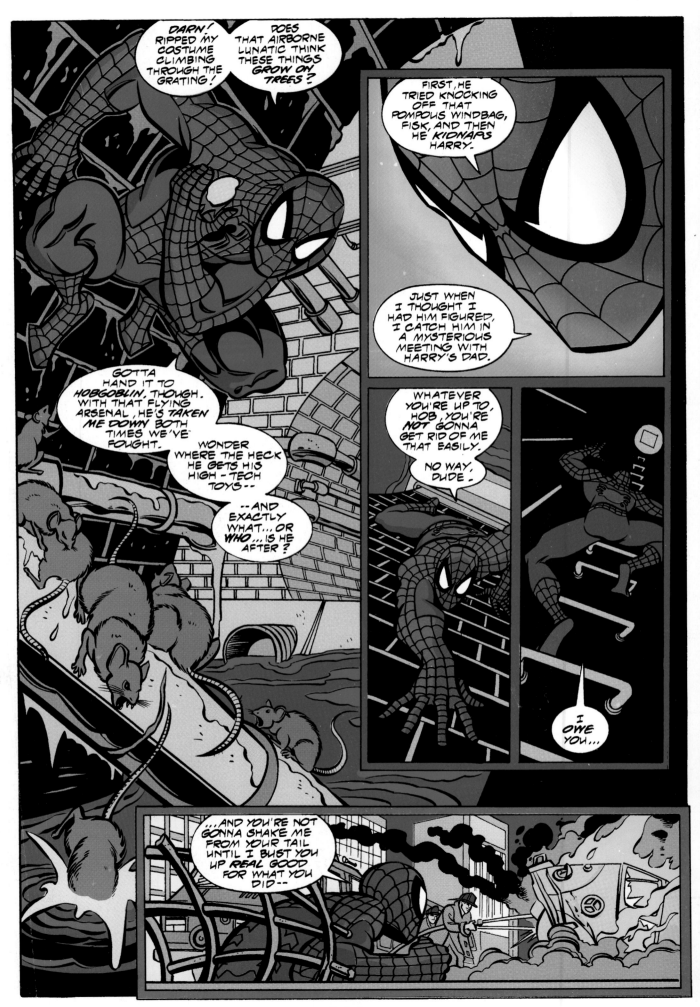

"-- TO AUNT MAY."

H-HOW IS SHE?

AL ROUGH MEDICAL CENTER MAIN ENTRANCE

DR. SHAFFNER SAID THERE'S NO CHANGE. I'VE BEEN WITH HER SINCE YOU LEFT, PETER.

IF I HADN'T DECIDED TO ROOM WITH HARRY OSBORN, NONE OF THIS WOULD'VE HAPPENED.

AW, WHAT'S THE USE...

LOOK, MJ, I REALLY APPRECIATE EVERYTHING YOU'VE DONE, BUT WHY DON'T YOU GO HOME AND GET SOME SLEEP? I'LL STAY.

YOU DON'T HAVE TO THANK ME. I DON'T MIND BEING HERE.

BESIDES, YOU'D BETTER GET BACK TO WORK...

YOU KNOW JAMESON. HE'S PROBABLY OUT LOOKING FOR ANOTHER FREELANCE PHOTOGRAPHER RIGHT NOW.

THANKS, MJ. THIS REALLY MEANS A LOT TO AUNT MAY... AND TO ME.

I'LL BE BACK LATER. 'BYE.

THIS IS ALL MY FAULT. OH, PLEASE LET MAY PULL THROUGH.

PLEASE LET HER BE ABLE TO HEAR HOW SORRY I AM...

THE ART DECO CHRYSLER BUILDING...HEADQUARTERS OF ONE DISREPUTABLE INDIVIDUAL.

TO MOST, HE IS KNOWN SIMPLY AS WEALTHY PHILANTHROPIST AND BUSINESSMAN WILSON FISK.

TO OTHERS, HE IS THE HEART AND SOUL OF A VAST CRIMINAL EMPIRE AS THE TYRANNICAL KINGPIN.

TONIGHT HE PLAYS HOST TO A VERY UNUSUAL GUEST...

I SEE YOU SAVOR MY TRAPPINGS OF POWER...

NOT JUST THE TRAPPINGS. I LIKE THE PRESTIGE AND INFLUENCE THAT YOU ENJOY, TOO.

BUT I'M NOT HERE TO MAKE SMALL TALK, FISK. THIS IS THE SECOND TIME I'M ASKING TO GET PAID FOR SERVICES RENDERED. DON'T SAY "NO" AGAIN.

REST ASSURED YOU'LL GET WHAT'S COMING TO YOU. FIRST, ALLOW ME TO SHOW YOU SOMETHING...

A VIDEO OF YOU AND NORMAN OSBORN, CUTTING A DEAL.

A DEAL TO DESTROY ME.

IS THIS THE GRATITUDE YOU SHOW?

AS OF NOW, HOBGOBLIN, YOU ARE AND SHALL BE--

--TERMINATED!

GUARDS! GET HIM!

I TOOK YOU IN EVEN AFTER DISCOVERING YOU HAD BEEN HIRED BY NORMAN TO KILL ME.

I ALLOWED YOU TO BE PART OF MY PLAN FOR REVENGE AND REDEEM YOURSELF BY KIDNAPPING NORMAN'S SON.

AND THEN OUR FIRST DISAGREEMENT DRIVES YOU TO DOUBLE-CROSS ME?

ENOUGH!

I'VE WORKED TOO HARD AND PLANNED TOO MUCH FOR YOU TO PULL THE RUG OUT FROM UNDER ME!

C'MON, FATSO! GIVE IT YOUR BEST SHOT!

VRRRR

"... HARRY OSBORN!"

M-MY FATHER PAID THE RANSOM! WHY WON'T YOU LET ME GO FREE?

FREE? NOTHING WITH ME IS EVER FREE!

YOU ARE MINE-- AND SO IS ALL OF CRIME CENTRAL!

WITH THIS TECHNOLOGY, I DON'T JUST OBSERVE... I CONTROL INFORMATION!

AND THE BETTER I CONTROL IT, THE WEALTHIER I'LL BECOME!

EVERYTHING'S WIRED TO THOSE PANELS BELOW... POWER. WATER. SECURITY. I CAN STAY HERE... FOREVER!

T-THEN WHAT DO YOU WANT FROM MY FATHER?

I WANT REVENGE!

REVENGE FOR FIRING ME! REVENGE FOR TREATING ME LIKE A TWO-BIT PUNK! REVENGE FOR UNDERESTIMATING MY ABILITIES!

AND THANKS TO YOU, DEAR HARRY, I'M GOING TO GET IT!

SHORTLY...

YOUR WING'S GREAT. IT HELPED ME DESTROY HIM, JUST LIKE YOU ORIGINALLY WANTED...

BUT NOW THAT I'VE GOT THE KINGPIN'S EMPIRE, I WANT OSCORP, TOO.

ALL OF IT. NOT JUST YOUR INVENTIONS.

...IS THAT THE KIND OF LANGUAGE TO USE IN FRONT OF... YOUR SON?

WE'LL BE IN TOUCH. 'BYE FOR NOW.

YOU ARE NUTS! I'LL EXPOSE YOUR IDENTITY FOR THE WHOLE WORLD TO--

WAIT! HOBGOBLIN! YOU ROTTEN, LYING--

NOW, NOW, OSBORN...

I BELIEVE THE WORD YOU'RE LOOKING FOR IS TRAITOR.

FORTUNATELY, AS YOU CAN SEE, HOBGOBLIN'S REPORT OF MY DEMISE WAS SOMEWHAT EXAGGERATED.

HOW STUPID CAN YOU BE, OSBORN? WHAT KIND OF FATHER ARE YOU TO PUT YOUR SON IN SUCH JEOPARDY?

YOU TWO WERE TRYING TO BLEED ME DRY! I HAD TO MAKE A DEAL WITH HIM!

AND DON'T EVER TALK ABOUT MY SON HAVING A BAD FATHER--

STOP! THIS BICKERING IS TAKING US NOWHERE! IT'S TIME WE ADDRESSED OUR COMMON FOE-- THE HOBGOBLIN!

WE CAN GET TO HIM THROUGH A SECRET TUNNEL THAT LEADS BACK TO MY HEADQUARTERS. WE USED IT TO MAKE OUR ESCAPE.

WHAT WE NEED IS A WEAPON--A WEAPON THAT CAN STAND UP TO THAT RIG YOU BUILT FOR HOBGOBLIN. ANY IDEAS, OSBORN?

A WEAPON? I JUST MIGHT HAVE SOMETHING...

...OR PERHAPS I SHOULD SAY SOMEONE...

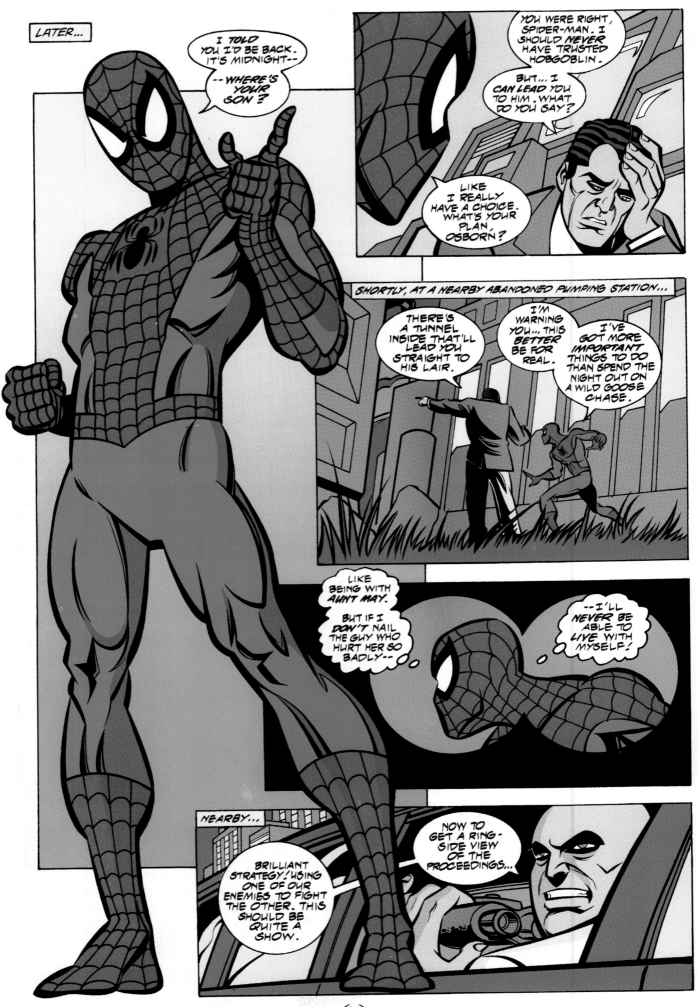

LOOK! LOOK AT WHAT YOU'VE DONE! IT'S ALL *RUINED!*

I'VE LOST *EVERYTHING* BECAUSE OF *YOU!*

NOT *QUITE*, HOBGOBLIN. YOU'VE STILL GOT YOUR *LIFE*.

...FOR THE *MOMENT*.

RELEASE HARRY OSBORN.

NOW.

SUCH A *REASONABLE* REQUEST, SPIDER-MAN. HOW CAN I *REFUSE*?

YOU *WANT* THE *BRAT*...

...YOU GOT 'IM! HAHAHA HAHA!

HARRY! HE'S GONNA *CRASH!*

SPIDER-MAN!

DON'T PANIC, HARRY! A TON OF FALLING GLASS AND STEEL! DO I STAND A CHANCE?

DOCTOR OCTOPUS

REAL NAME:
Otto Octavius

OCCUPATION: Formerly a top nuclear physicist, now a professional criminal

BASE OF OPERATIONS: A secret laboratory

WEAPONS: Four telescoping titanium-steel tentacles which became bonded to his body as the result of an accident when he was using them to handle radioactive material. The mechanical arms respond to his mental commands.

ALLIES: None. The warped genius prefers to work alone.

THE LIZARD

REAL NAME: Curt Connors

OCCUPATION: Doctor and scientist

BASE OF OPERATIONS: A laboratory in a New York skyscraper

WEAPONS: Following a freak accident during a bio-regenerative experiment, Dr Connors was transformed into the half-man half-reptile creature, The Lizard. The change is not permanent, Dr Connors only becoming the exceptionally strong Lizard at times of extreme stress.

ALLIES: While Spider-Man and The Lizard are deadly foes, Dr Curt Connors and Peter Parker are close friends (although Dr Connors doesn't suspect Peter's secret identity).

SPIDER-MAN

FACT FILES

DOUBLE TROUBLE!

by Alan Cowsill

"Peter, I can't believe you talked me into this," yawned Mary Jane.

Peter Parker realised he'd made a mistake. In trying to keep his date with Mary Jane and hear Dr Curt Connors' lecture on genetic manipulation, he'd combined the two but it wasn't one of his better ideas.

"Listen, Tiger," whispered Mary Jane, "we shouldn't be in a stuffy old lecture hall on a Friday night."

Peter was about to agree when a familiar sensation went through him…his amazing spider-sense. Suddenly, a huge explosion blasted a hole in the far wall of the stage, forcing Dr Connors to shield his son Billy from flying debris.

People were screaming and fleeing from the hall. On his feet, Peter was looking for somewhere to change to Spider-Man.

"MJ, get out of here!" he called above the mayhem. "I'm going to take some photos!"

Mary Jane narrowed her eyes. "Okay," she said, "but if you pull one of your vanishing acts again there'll be trouble." A crowd of panic-stricken people separated them and Peter seized the chance to flee down the stairs towards the stage

I can't believe it, he thought. *I'm running from Mary Jane and towards danger. There's something wrong with my life…*

At the side of the stage, out of sight of everyone, Peter changed into his Spider-Man costume and raced out onto the stage.

"Stay away from my son!" Connors was shouting at a figure emerging through the smoke and fallen masonry.

Spidey recognised him at once. "Doctor Octopus!" he exclaimed. "I guess you're not a science fan!"

"On the contrary, you webbed menace," snarled Doc Ock. "I'm here for Dr Connors. I have need of his services and his new Genetic Destabiliser."

One of Octopus's mechanical arms curled itself around the struggling doctor, a second stretching out towards Billy. Two more mechanical limbs arched towards Spider-Man who leapt out of the way.

"Listen, Doc," he said, "I always beat you in the end. Why not give up now and save us both a lot of time?"

"Impertinent fool!" Octopus roared, launching himself at the web-slinger. "You've never defeated me! Never!"

"You'll have to do better than that," replied Spidey, ducking with ease under one of the arms.

"I already have," Doctor Octopus smiled as a steel tentacle struck Spider-Man hard, sending him hurtling off the stage and into a pile of rubble.

"Lucky shot," Spider-Man murmured, just in time to see Octopus escaping through the hole in the wall. He threw a spider tracer onto his enemy's back but by the time he had managed to pull himself free of the rubble, Octopus had disappeared, taking Dr Connors and Billy with him.

At Dr Connors' lab high in a nearby Manhattan skyscraper, he was pleading with Doctor Octopus to let Billy go. "He's done nothing wrong…" he was saying.

"My dear doctor," Octopus replied slowly, "if I were to release him, how would I ever convince you to use your Genetic Destabiliser on me?"

"On you?! You're mad!" cried Connors. "The Destabiliser is for helping sick people, not for…"

"…Increasing the strength of someone like myself?" offered Octopus. "I'm sure you will understand, being a scientist yourself, and someone who has battled against Spider-Man…"

"That wasn't me!" Connors cut in. "That was the Lizard!"

"Yes, I know all about your little transformation and how, in attempting to regenerate your lost arm, you turned yourself into that deadly creature," Octopus said. "I also know that your new machine can do the same thing and increase powers."

"Never! I won't help you!"

Doctor Octopus smiled, carefully pushing Billy against the wall. "What would happen if I were to lose my temper?"

"Hurt him and I'll…"

"Do not threaten me," warned Octopus, curling a mechanical arm menacingly around Connors' throat. "I am the master here and you will do as I order."

Connors knew Octopus was right. There was nothing he could do…at least, nothing Dr Curt Connors could do. Grimly, he realised that, no matter what the awful consequences might be, there was only one option.

"Okay, I'll help you," he sighed, starting the machine's controls. Octopus watched victoriously as it hummed into life. Then it moved into position, a bright light covering Connors, whose agonising scream cut through the laboratory.

"Connors! What are you doing?" demanded Octopus.

"Protecting my son," hissed Connors, doubled up in pain. Scales appeared on his body and his missing arm was growing back as he became once more…the Lizard!

With the terrible transformation complete, he turned to face Doctor Octopus. His strong reptilian tail lashed out, sending Octopus crashing against a bank of computers.

"Dad!" cried Billy, terrified at the sight of his father's change.

The Lizard seemed to hesitate for a moment and it was all the time Octopus needed. Two mechanical arms slithered forward and grabbed him.

Then there was a familiar voice from above the door: "What's this? A Bad Guys' Convention? Gee, if you'd told me, I would have had a speech ready!"

"Spider-Man!" called Billy, running to him. "You've got to help my dad!"

"I'll try, Billy," Spidey promised. "You get out of here."

But before Billy could escape through

the door, one of Doctor Octopus's metal tentacles slammed it shut.

"The boy stays!" he exclaimed, turning to the Lizard. "Well, my slithering friend, what say we join together in smashing Spider-Man to a pulp?"

"Er...do I get a vote?" asked the wall-crawler, pulling Billy behind him.

"Dessstroy him!" spat the Lizard, hurling himself at Spider-Man.

Spidey tried to reason with the furious reptile as he pushed Billy out of the way. "Dr Connors, you've got to fight the Lizard! I know you're in there somewhere."

"Not thisss time, insssect!" the Lizard hissed. "The machine has made me ssstronger than ever!"

Spidey knew he was in trouble. In his previous encounters with Doctor Octopus and the Lizard he had managed to defeat them both separately, but now they were fighting side by side.

The Lizard leapt at him, the half-human creature's fists hammering home blow after blow. Then one of Doc Ock's tentacles wrapped itself tightly around Spider-Man.

"You're finished, you meddling fool!" he laughed. He hurled the wall-crawler against the huge laser, sending it sliding across the floor towards Billy. As Spider-Man fired his webbing at the machine, a green blur darted past and the Lizard pushed Billy clear. Seeing his son in danger, Dr Connors had

somehow managed to gain control of the Lizard's body.

The machine careered into the wall, smashed and broken, wires and tubes hanging out everywhere. A computerised voice crackled, "Danger! Genetic breach! Laser will explode in twenty-five seconds..."

"We've got to get out of here!" called Spider-Man.

"I...can't..." moaned the Lizard, speaking with Connors' strained voice. "The Lizard...is regaining...control. You've got to take Billy with you..."

"No!" Billy cried.

"Twenty seconds to detonation," announced the mechanical voice.

"I will not let you leave," said Octopus. "I intend to have control of Connors' machine!" He shot two mechanical arms at the web-slinger but webbing struck them both, binding them together. Another tentacle knocked Spider-Man to the floor. Doctor Octopus approached his enemy.

"Fifteen seconds..."

"Doc, the laser's blocking the door!" Spidey exclaimed. "We have to make another way out or we'll die!"

"If I must die, I'll take you with me!" declared Octopus.

"Leave him alone!" yelled Billy, rushing to help Spidey and pounding his fists on Octopus's back.

As Octopus pushed him away, the Lizard rushed forward, ordering him away from the boy. Connors was fighting to keep his human side dominant.

"Get Billy out, Spider-Man!" The determination in his voice made the web-swinger act. He swept the boy up in his arms and dived through a large window, back first to protect Billy from the shattering glass.

"Two seconds..."

As Spidey disappeared through the window, the laser exploded, its radiation bathing the laboratory in an eerie green neon light. Spider-Man, clinging to the wall outside, Billy cradled in his arms, shot a strand of webbing back through the window and felt it connect with something.

The Lizard came tumbling out, pulling Spider-Man and the boy down with him. As the three fell through the air, the reptile began to transform back into Dr Connors. With the ground rushing up to meet them, Spider-Man hastily sprayed his amazing webbing below, forming a net which caught them all safely.

Just then, a charred and smoking Doctor Octopus came hurtling down towards them, crashing through the net and enveloping Spider-Man in his tentacles, pulling the wall-crawler down with him.

"I'm taking you with me, you interfering creepy-crawly!" he cursed.

Dr Connors and Billy were holding onto the remains of the net, but Spidey knew they wouldn't be able to stay there for long. Anger and frustration coursed through him. Even though the Lizard was one of his most fearsome foes, he couldn't let him and Billy come to harm.

Tearing an arm free of Octopus's tentacles, he sprayed webbing straight into his enemy's face and pushed himself free, clinging to the wall as Octopus continued to fall. With incredible speed, Spider-Man sprayed webbing to the ground, providing Octopus with a soft landing, before tying him securely with a strong web strand to make sure he couldn't escape. The cheers from the crowd which had gathered on the street drowned out the villain's curses.

"Keep an eye on him," Spidey told a nearby cop. "There are still two people up there who need my help." He raced back up the wall to rescue Dr Connors and Billy.

Minutes later, Spidey set them both down on the ground as the police led Octopus away. A dazed Dr Connors gave his thanks.

"No problem," said Spider-Man. "Take care of yourself and Billy."

He was about to swing away when he caught sight of Mary Jane in the crowd. Darting back to the stage in the hall, he quickly changed back into his normal clothes and emerged as Peter Parker, taking photos as he did so.

"Peter!" called Mary Jane, her arms folded. "Somehow, I thought I'd find you here." He could tell she wasn't pleased with him.

"Sorry, MJ…" he began, desperately trying to think of an excuse.

"No excuses," she said. "If this is your idea of a good night out, there's only one thing for it."

Peter's heart sank. *She's going to dump me*, he thought. *I've had this coming. Spider-Man always gets in the way.*

"No more science lectures," she decided, kissing him on the cheek. "Next time we're going dancing. Got it, Tiger?"

"Got it," Peter smiled, hoping none of his enemies liked dancing!

GOOD EVENING. I'M MADAME HARKNESS AND I'VE BEEN *WAITING* FOR YOU.

PLEASE... COME INTO MY PARLOR AND WE CAN BEGIN.

WOWEE! YOU'RE *RIGHT*, MJ. WE'LL STAY. I *WOULDN'T* WANT YOU TO WASTE YOUR MONEY, AND IT WOULD BE RUDE--

PEEETER...

YOUR COMPANION TELLS ME YOU ARE *SHY* AND *WITHDRAWN*, MR. PARKER.

EXPERIENCE HAS SHOWN ME THAT IT IS THOSE SUCH AS YOURSELF WHO *HARBOR* THE *DARKEST SECRETS.*

LOOK, IF IT'S THE MONEY YOU'RE WORRIED ABOUT--

NO, NO-- THIS IS *GREAT!* YOU LEAVE IF YOU WANT TO, BUT I'M GONNA *STAY...*

LIKE MOST YOUNG MEN, WITHIN YOU BURNS THE *SOUL* OF AN *ADVENTURER...*

...*SOARING* ABOVE THE MUNDANE, *WEBBING* FROM INTRIGUE TO INTRIGUE, *TEMPTING* EVIL AND FIGHTING FOR THE COMMON GOOD...

AND YET... YOURS ARE *NOT* IDLE DAYDREAMS. YOU *DO* POSSESS THE *POWER* TO *ACT* UPON SUCH FANTASIES, DON'T YOU, MR. PARKER?

"*MIDTOWN HIGH'S ONLY PROFESSIONAL WALLFLOWER*' IS HOW THE OTHER STUDENTS TAUNTED ME...

POWERS? SOAR AND *WEB?* DOES SHE *KNOW?*

NO WAY. IT *CAN'T* BE. *NO ONE* KNOWS MY *SECRET!*

BUT POWER IS *NEVER* ENOUGH. YOU SILENTLY SEEK *RECOGNITION* FOR YOUR *ENVIABLE* ABILITIES--

--AND IN DOING SO, OFTEN EXERCISE POOR JUDGMENT...

I DON'T LIKE THIS ONE BIT. SHE'S TOO DARN NEAR THE TRUTH FOR HER ACCURACY TO BE COINCIDENCE.

HOW COULD SHE POSSIBLY *KNOW* ABOUT THE PROBLEMS MY EGO CAUSED ME?

" FOR *SOMEONE* WHO SEEMED TO BE MORE SPIDER THAN HUMAN, I KNEW I COULD TURN A FAST BUCK BY TAKING MY NEW POWERS PUBLIC.

" MOVIE PRODUCERS, INTERVIEWERS, COMIC BOOK PUBLISHERS... I HAD THEM ALL *WANTING* A PIECE OF ME.

" BUT ON THE NIGHT OF MY FIRST NATIONAL TELEVISION APPEARANCE...

" ...I LET A *PUNK* THIEF ESCAPE THE STUDIO WITHOUT EVEN LIFTING AN ARM TO STOP HIM.

THE CHRONICLE
SPIDER-MAN PLAYS
OCKED HOUSES

TV GUIDE

" IN THE WEEKS THAT FOLLOWED, I BECAME THE SENSATION OF THE NATION...

DAILY VOICE
WHO IS THE SPIDER-MA

EVIEWER
ER-MAN
INS

" ...BUT UPON RETURNING HOME FROM A TV APPEARANCE ONE NIGHT--

" -- A POLICEMAN STATIONED OUTSIDE MY HOUSE TOLD ME THAT UNCLE BEN HAD BEEN *MURDERED.*

" MY WORLD *FELL APART* IN THAT SINGULAR MOMENT. ALL I COULD THINK OF WAS *VENGEANCE*...

" A SELFISH DECISION THAT WOULD LATER COME TO *HAUNT* ME.

"I CORNERED THE KILLER AT THE OLD WATERFRONT WAREHOUSE.

"HE DIDN'T STAND A CHANCE...

"BUT FOR THE SECOND TIME THAT NIGHT, MY WORLD CAME CRASHING DOWN UPON ME AS I DISCOVERED--

"--THAT BEN'S MURDERER WAS THE THIEF I LET RUN PAST ME AT THE TV STUDIO...THE ONE I DIDN'T STOP WHEN I HAD THE CHANCE.

"I'VE LIVED WITH THAT GUILT EACH AND EVERY DAY OF MY LIFE..."

DESPITE YOUR MISTAKES, YOU'VE LEARNED WELL THE LESSON THAT WITH GREAT POWER THERE MUST ALSO COME GREAT RESPONSIBILITY.

G-GREAT POWER? GREAT RESPONSIBILITY?

SOUNDS LIKE YOU'VE BEEN READING TOO MANY COMICS, MADAME. ARE WE FINISHED?

YES, BUT YOU SEEM DISTRESSED. WAS IT SOMETHING I SAID?

N-NOT AT ALL. I GUESS THE AIR IN HERE WAS...UH, BEGINNING TO GET TO ME. THANKS AND...'BYE!

IT MAY'VE BEEN A MAJOR WASTE OF MONEY, BUT IT WAS WORTH SEEING THE LOOK ON YOUR FACE WHEN SHE WAS DISHING THAT NONSENSE!

ALL THAT TALK ABOUT "SPECIAL POWERS" AND ABILITIES...! SHE DIDN'T KNOW WHAT SHE WAS TALKING ABOUT!

OR DID SHE?

THE END